The Berenstain Bears' MAKE-AND-DO BOOK

by Stan & Jan Berenstain

Activities designed by Marion Needham Krupp

Random House · New York

2 3 4 5 6 7 8 9 0

This book is full of wonderful things to make and do. Almost everything in it can be made from things you already have in your house. You will also need a pair of scissors, paste, cellophane tape, and colored pencils, crayons, or felt-tip markers. The ink in some markers goes through the paper, so test your markers on a corner of the page to make sure that yours don't do that.

Some things in this book are easier to do than others, so ask a grownup for help when you need it. And whenever you use scissors or any sharp tool, ask a grownup to help you.

Watch out for Officer Grizzly! He's there to warn you when there is an activity on the back of a page that you will cut up. Don't cut anything out until you have checked the next page first.

Here are some of the things you can make:

A Bird Feeder	A Honey Graham Cottage
The Bear Family Tree House	A High-Flying Bear Kite
Finger Puppets	A Pomander Ball
The Bear Country Schoolhouse	A Necklace and Rings
A Dancing Papa Bear	The Bear Family Car
A Bear Mobile	A Grizzbee
Bear Marks	Tops to Spin

Plus much, much more, including games and puzzles.

2

Dancing Papa Bear

You will need:
Thin cardboard
Hole puncher or sharp pencil
4 paper brads
A length of string about 24 inches long
Needlepoint needle

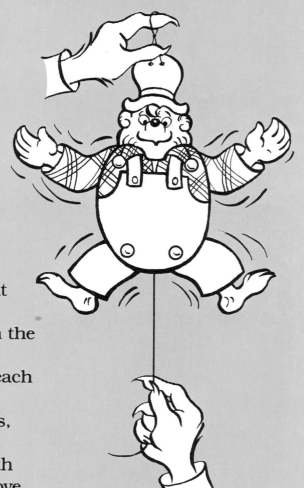

1. Color all the parts of Papa Bear. Then cut page 5 from the book and paste it to the cardboard. (Ask a grownup to help you with the scissors.)

2. When the paste is dry, carefully cut out each part of Papa Bear.

3. Punch out the big holes in the arms, legs, and body where marked.

4. Attach the arms and legs to the body with the brads. (Make sure the arms and legs move easily around the brads.)

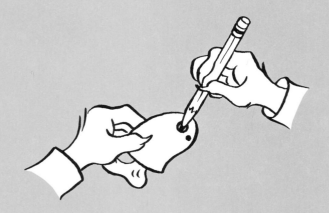

(Continued on page 4)

5. Thread the needle with the string and make a large knot.

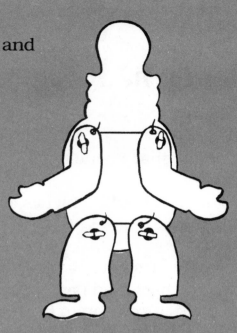

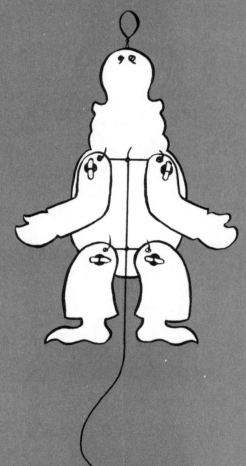

6. Thread the string through the small holes in the arms. Make sure it is straight and tie off with a knot. Tie the legs in the same way.

7. With the arms and legs hanging down, tie a long "pull" string to the middle of the cross-strings between the arms and legs. Leave a pull string of about 5—6 inches hanging down.

8. Punch holes through the top of Papa's hat and tie a loop of string to hold him by.

Make Papa dance by pulling on the hanging string.

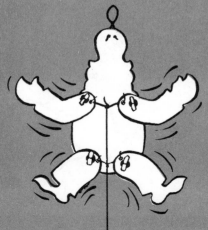

4

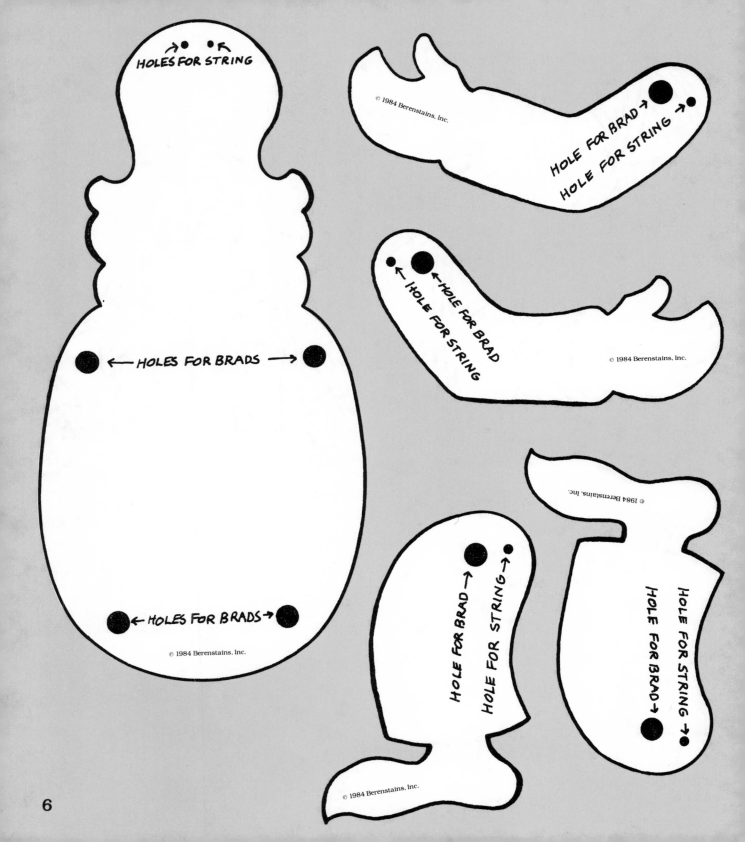

HOLES FOR STRING

© 1984 Berenstains, Inc.

HOLE FOR BRAD →
HOLE FOR STRING →

← HOLE FOR BRAD
HOLE FOR STRING

© 1984 Berenstains, Inc.

← HOLES FOR BRADS →

← HOLES FOR BRADS →

© 1984 Berenstains, Inc.

HOLE FOR BRAD →
HOLE FOR STRING →

© 1984 Berenstains, Inc.

© 1984 Berenstains, Inc.

HOLE FOR STRING
HOLE FOR BRAD →

Honey-Fruit Nog

Here's a delicious drink that is so simple and quick to make, even Papa Bear can do it!

You will need:
1 egg
1 tablespoon honey
2 cups pineapple or orange juice
1 cup milk
1 mashed banana or 6 large mashed strawberries
1 8-ounce container of plain or fruit yogurt
Large mixing bowl
Egg beater
4 tall glasses

Beat the egg until nice and frothy.
Add all the other ingredients and beat well.
Serve in tall glasses.

Bear Tree House

When the Bear family needed a new home, Papa Bear made them a wonderful tree house. You can make one too.

1. Color and then cut out all the parts of the tree house on pages 9, 11, 13, and 15. (Ask a grownup to help you with the scissors.)

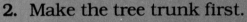

2. Make the tree trunk first.
3. Make the branches and attach with tape to the tree trunk.

4. Make the treetop and paste the chimney to it.

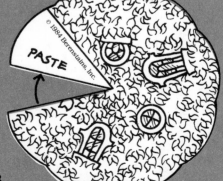

5. Fold the front steps and attach to tree trunk with tape.

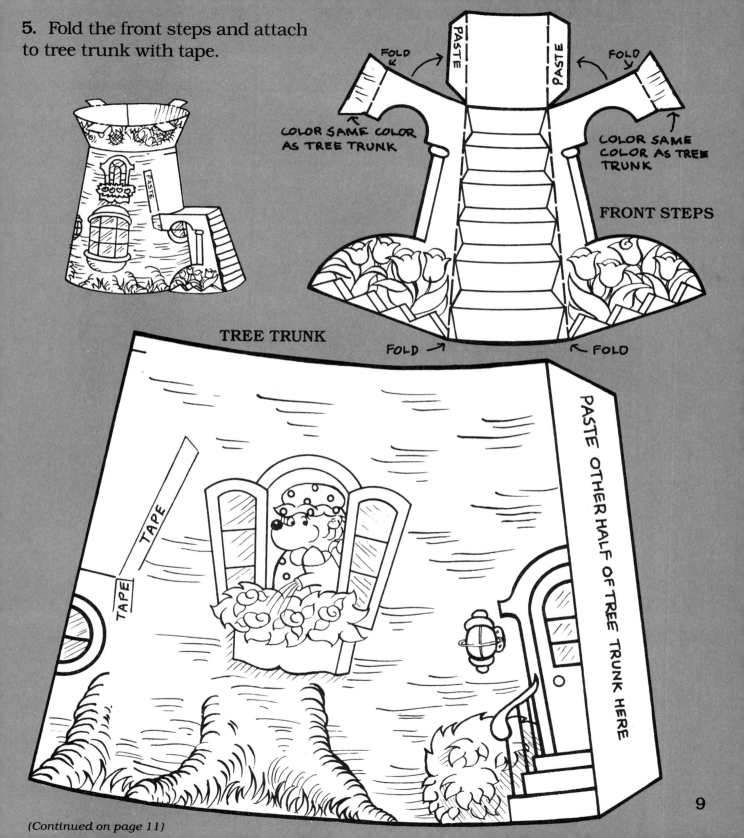

FOLD

PASTE

PASTE

FOLD

COLOR SAME COLOR AS TREE TRUNK

COLOR SAME COLOR AS TREE TRUNK

FRONT STEPS

FOLD →

← FOLD

TREE TRUNK

TAPE

TAPE

PASTE OTHER HALF OF TREE TRUNK HERE

9

(Continued on page 11)

FOLD

FOLD

FOLD

FOLD

FOLD

FOLD

© 1984 Berenstains, Inc.

© 1984 Berenstains, Inc.

10

6. Fold the door and attach to trunk above steps.

PASTE

FOLD

FOLD

PASTE

PASTE

FRONT DOOR

COLOR
SAME AS
TREE
TRUNK

FOLD

FOLD

COLOR
SAME
AS
TREE
TRUNK

TREE TRUNK

TAPE

TAPE

PASTE OTHER HALF OF TREE TRUNK HERE

(Continued on page 13)

11

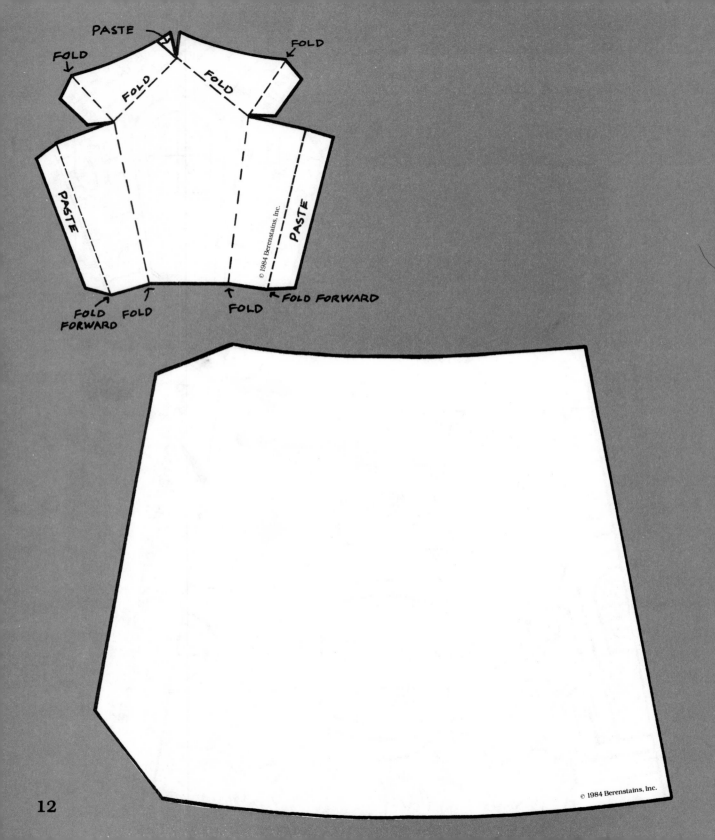

PASTE

FOLD   FOLD

FOLD   FOLD

PASTE   PASTE

© 1984 Berenstains, Inc.

FOLD
FORWARD   FOLD   FOLD   FOLD FORWARD

© 1984 Berenstains, Inc.

12

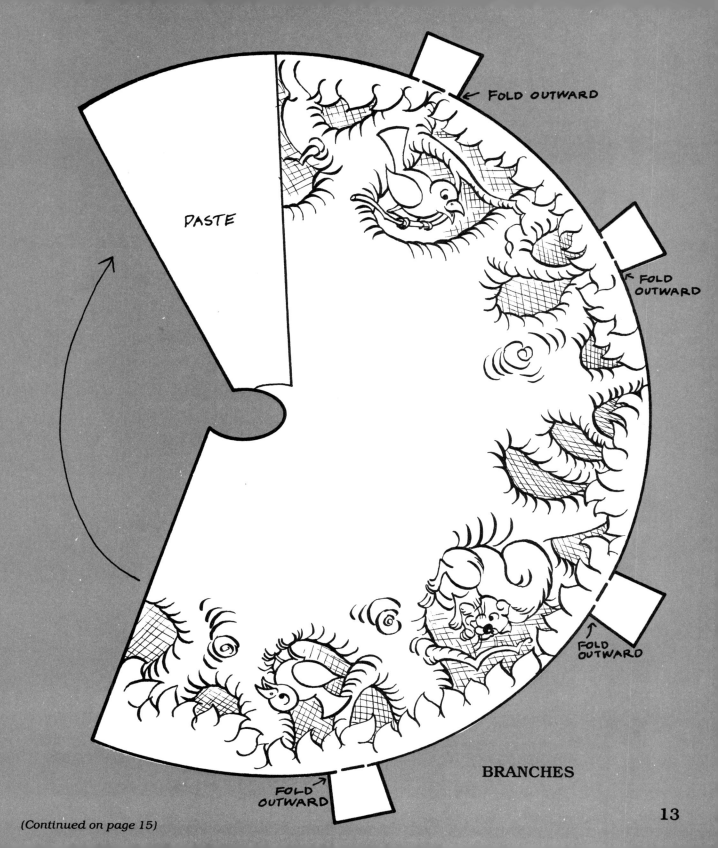

PASTE

← FOLD OUTWARD

← FOLD OUTWARD

FOLD OUTWARD

FOLD OUTWARD

BRANCHES

(Continued on page 15)

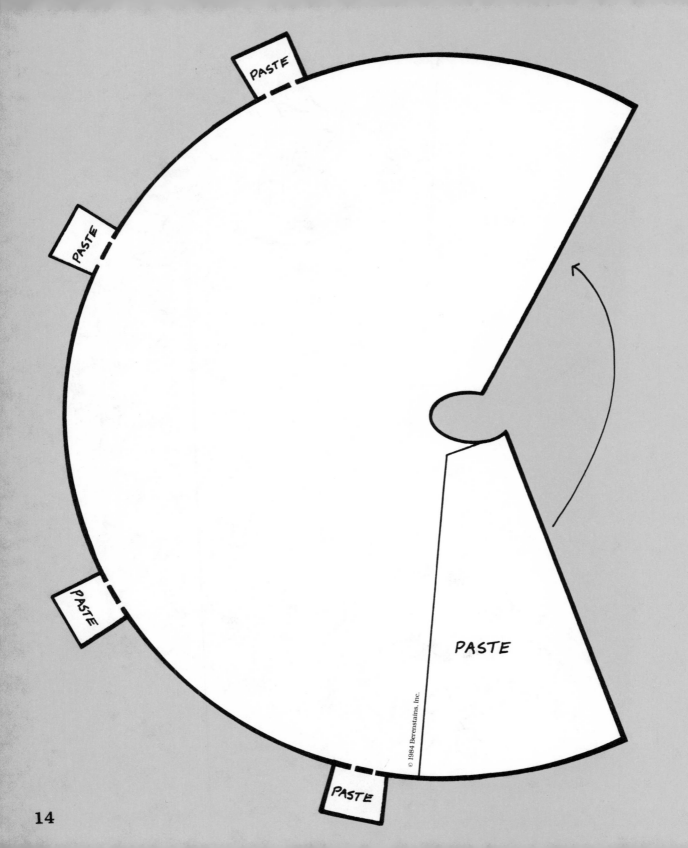

PASTE

PASTE

PASTE

PASTE

PASTE

© 1984 Berenstains, Inc.

14

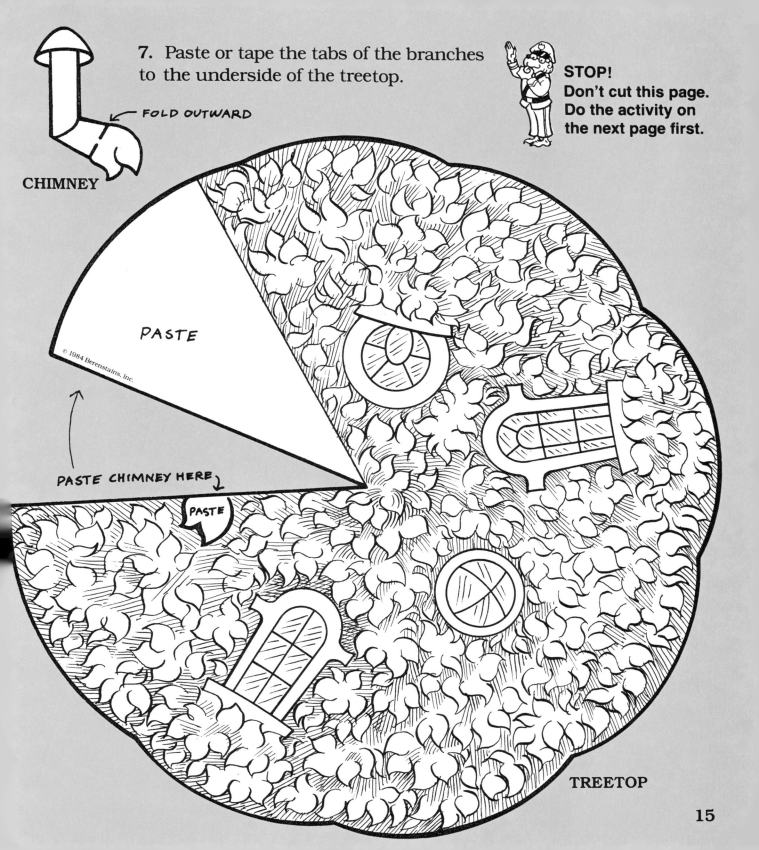

7. Paste or tape the tabs of the branches to the underside of the treetop.

FOLD OUTWARD

CHIMNEY

STOP! Don't cut this page. Do the activity on the next page first.

PASTE

© 1984 Berenstains, Inc.

PASTE CHIMNEY HERE

PASTE

TREETOP

Word Search

Papa Bear is always happy when he finds honey. In the word HONEY, the letters O and N stand next to each other. Look at the pictures and see if you can fill in the missing letters of other words with O and N in them. (To see if you got all the words right, turn to page 64.)

__ __ __ O N

__ __ __ __ __ O N

__ O N __

__ O N __ __ __

__ __ __ O N

__ __ O N

__ __ O N

__ __ __ __ O N __

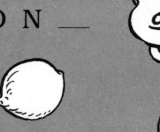

Lucky Bear Rings

Make one for yourself or your friends!

STOP!
Don't cut this page.
Do the activity on
the next page first.

You will need:
4 flat buttons about the size of the pictures of the Bear
   family (a raised edge on a button will make a nice
   frame for the picture)
2 colored pipe cleaners, each cut in half

1. Color the pictures for the ring tops
and then cut them out. (Ask a grownup
to help you with the scissors.)
2. Thread a piece of pipe cleaner
through the buttonholes.
3. Wrap the pipe cleaner around your
finger to measure for size. (Don't make it
tight!)
4. Twist the ends of the pipe cleaner
together and snip off the extra pieces.
5. Paste a picture onto the button.

Now you have a lucky Bear ring.

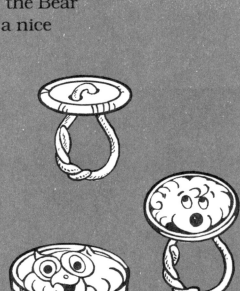

If you want to make a brooch instead:
1. Thread the pipe cleaner through the
buttonholes.
2. Twist the ends of the pipe cleaner
together close to the back of the button.
3. Snip off the extra pieces.
4. Fasten a safety pin to the back of the
button.
5. Paste a Bear family picture onto the
button.

Bird Feeder

The Bear family has a bird feeder in their yard.
You can have one too.

You will need:
Empty milk carton (half gallon works best)
Hole puncher or sharp pencil
Twig or wooden dowel 4–5 inches longer
   than the width of the carton
Length of twine or yarn

1. Rinse the milk carton out
so that it is nice and clean.
2. Cut a window in the side of
the carton. (Ask a grownup to
help.)
3. Use the hole puncher or the
point of the pencil to make a hole
in the top of the carton for the
twine.
4. Make a hole on either side of
the carton below the window for
the twig or dowel. (Ask a grownup
to help.)

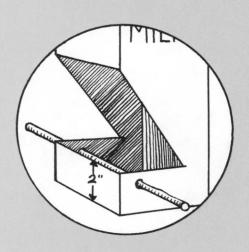

5. Use the pencil point to poke a
few small holes in the bottom of
the carton so that rainwater will
drain out.
6. Push the twig or dowel
through the holes on the sides of
the carton and let it stick out
about 2 inches on each side.

18

7. Tie the twine or yarn through the hole at the top of the feeder.

8. Fill your feeder with birdseed or bread crumbs and hang it securely from a tree.

You will get lots of visitors!

Bear Family Car

1. Color and cut out the windshield (both sides), car, and figures (ask a grownup to help you with the scissors).
2. Fold each figure along the center fold and paste back and front together.
3. Fold base backward and paste figure onto car where marked.
4. Fold and paste car where marked.
5. Attach windshield as shown in illustration.

FOLD BACK AND PASTE TOGETHER

PASTE

PASTE TO CAR

ATTACH WINDSHIELD

PASTE FIGURES IN CAR

PASTE

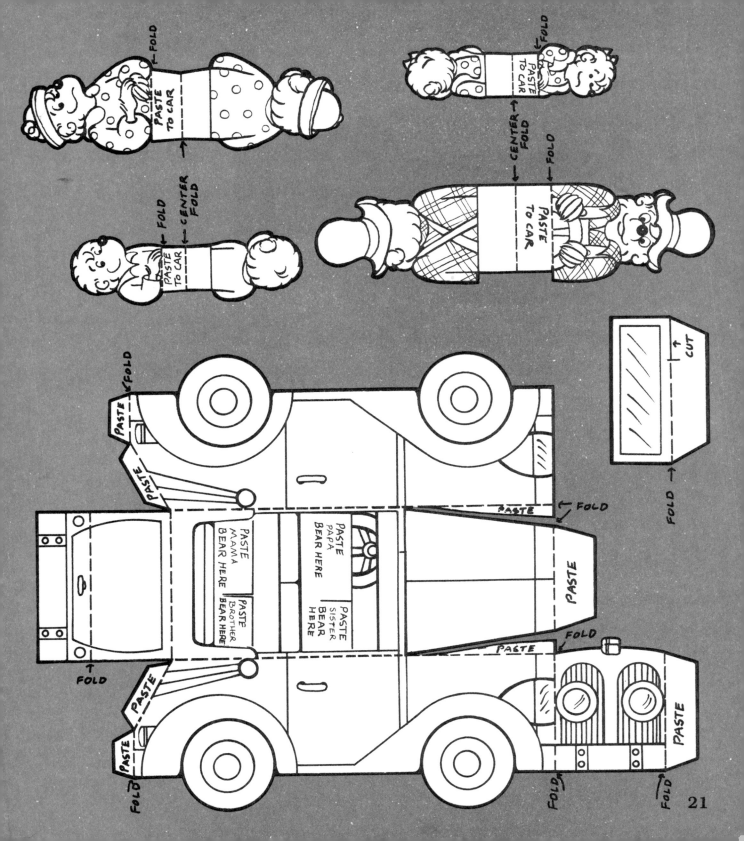

21

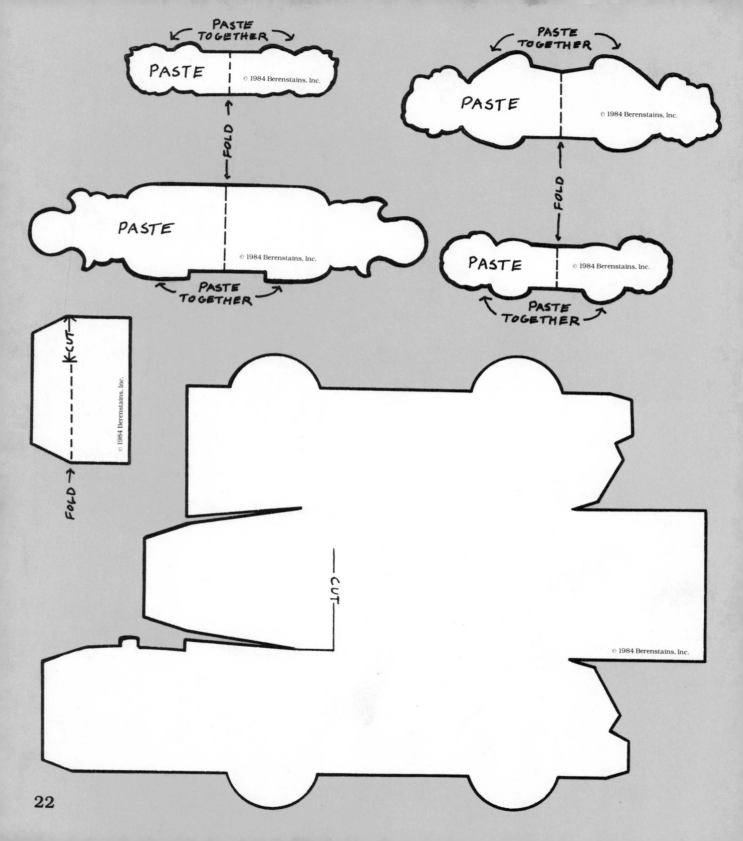

Bear Door Signs

Everyone wants to be alone sometimes. Here are two signs to hang on your door when you don't want to be disturbed.

© 1984 Berenstains, Inc.

1. Color both sides of the sign.
2. Cut out the sign carefully. (Ask a grownup to help you with the scissors.)
3. Punch out the holes at the top of the sign. Thread some brightly colored yarn through the holes.
4. Make a large double knot at each end of the yarn.
5. Hang your sign on your doorknob when you don't want to be disturbed.

The Bear Family

Here is the Bear family! Color the figures on this page and on pages 27 and 29 and then cut them out. (Ask a grownup to help you with the scissors.)

FOLD

BROTHER BEAR

FOLD →

MAMA BEAR

FOLD ↗   FOLD ↗

(Continued on page 27)

© 1984 Berenstains, Inc.

© 1984 Berenstains, Inc.

SISTER BEAR

FOLD

FOLD

FOLD

FOLD

PAPA BEAR

FOLD

FOLD

(Continued on page 29)

27

© 1984 Berenstains, Inc.

© 1984 Berenstains, Inc.

© 1984 Berenstains, Inc.

28

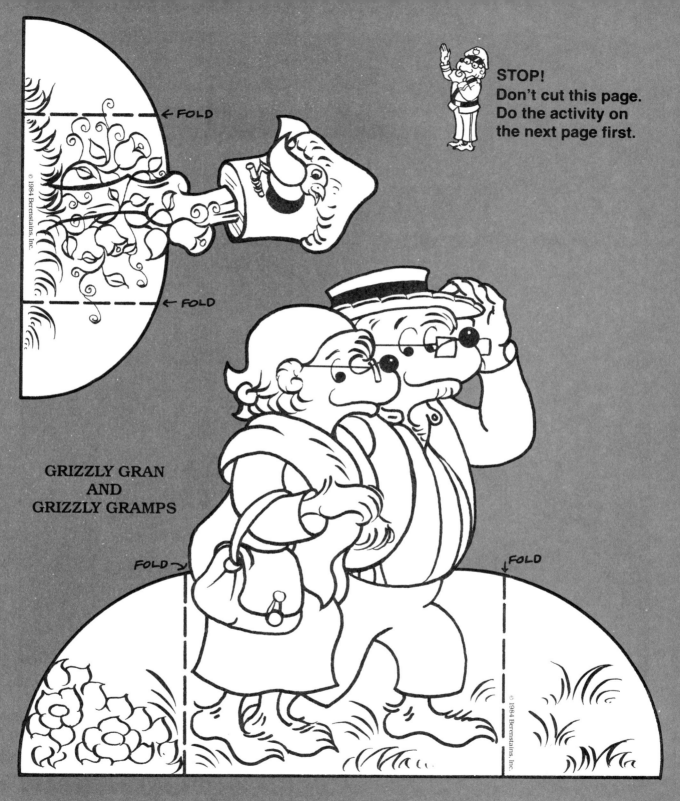

← FOLD

← FOLD

© 1984 Berenstains, Inc.

STOP!
Don't cut this page.
Do the activity on
the next page first.

GRIZZLY GRAN
AND
GRIZZLY GRAMPS

FOLD →

↓ FOLD

© 1984 Berenstains, Inc.

A Honey-Hunt Maze

Papa Bear knows there's a honey tree in these woods, but he's not sure how to find it. Help Papa Bear find the honey tree without crossing any lines. (To see if you found the right path, turn to page 64.

Bear Paw Shadows

One night when Gran was baby-sitting Sister and Brother Bear, she showed them how to make Bear Paw Shadows using her paws and a flashlight.

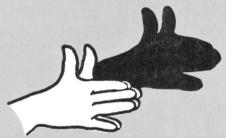

You will need a friend to shine the flashlight onto a blank wall while you make the shadows. Hold your fingers in the positions shown and you can make lots of different animals.

Wiggle your fingers to make this rabbit move his ears. If you move your thumb his nose will wiggle.

Hold your palms together and move your little fingers to make this dog speak. You can make his ears move as well.

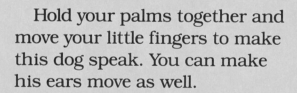

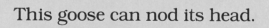

This goose can nod its head.

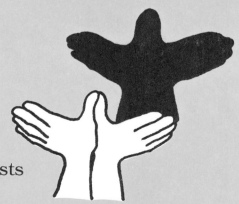

Keep your thumbs and wrists together to make this bird. He can fly!

Honey Graham Cottage

One day, when Brother and Sister Bear were visiting Gran and Gramps, Gran showed them how to make a Honey Graham Cottage. You can make one too.

You will need:

4 graham crackers (and a few extra, in case a cracker
   breaks while you are making the cottage)
Candies, such as chocolate chips, sugar-coated gum
   (like Chiclets), cinnamon candies, M&M's, licorice,
   gumdrops, bubble gum, miniature marshmallows,
   jelly beans, and any other candy you like
1 piece of cardboard on which to stand the cottage
Newspaper to spread under your work area
Small serrated plastic knife
A damp paper towel
White icing (recipe follows)
Small bowl
Egg whisk or beater
1 egg white
1½ cups confectioners' sugar

WHEN THE RECIPE
SAYS ONE GRAHAM
CRACKER, USE
THIS MUCH:

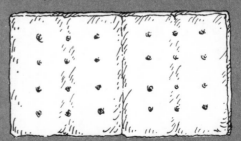

GRAHAM CRACKERS USUALLY
COME PACKAGED LIKE THIS:

To make the icing:

In the small bowl beat the egg white until it is foamy. (Ask a grownup to help you.) Add the confectioners' sugar, half a cup at a time, and mix it well. Continue to mix the icing until it is a little stiff and very white. (If the icing is too wet add more confectioners' sugar.) The icing dries quickly, so keep the bowl covered with the damp paper towel while you build the cottage.

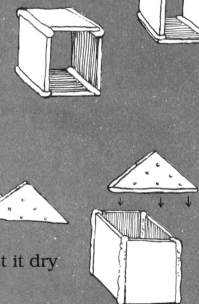

To make the cottage:

You will need four crackers to make the walls of the cottage.

1. Spread icing along the edges and stick the crackers together as shown. Leave to dry for 10 minutes.

2. Make the gable ends of the house by "sawing" a cracker in half diagonally. (Don't try to cut the crackers because they will break.) If you do break a cracker use a spare one and try again.

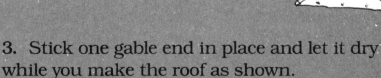

ICE
BOTH EDGES

3. Stick one gable end in place and let it dry while you make the roof as shown.

(Continued on page 34)

4. While the roof is drying, stick the second gable end in place. Leave it to dry.

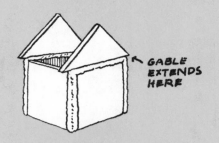

GABLE EXTENDS HERE

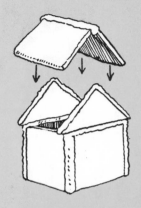

5. When the roof is dry, stick it on the house as shown. Leave to dry for 10 minutes while you cut the doors.

CUT HERE TO MAKE DOOR

6. Stick the doors on each end of the house.

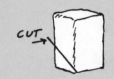

CUT

A PIECE OF BUBBLE GUM MAKES A GOOD CHIMNEY

7. Put the house on the cardboard base and decorate it.

8. Spread icing on one half of the roof at a time and decorate it as you wish. You can use chocolate chips, M&M's, cinnamon candies, or licorice cut to fit.

Make the house as beautiful as you wish.

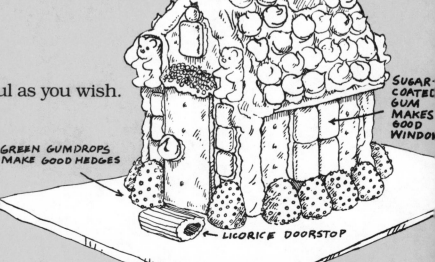

SUGAR-COATED GUM MAKES GOOD WINDOW

GREEN GUMDROPS MAKE GOOD HEDGES

← LICORICE DOORSTOP

Bear Necklace

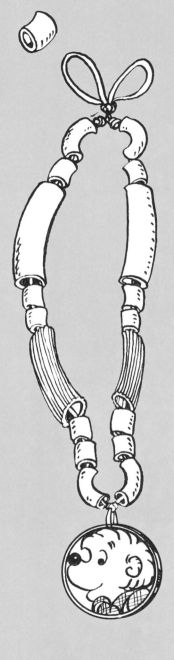

You will need:
Length of brightly colored yarn about 28 inches long
Large flat button with holes, about
 the same size as one of the decals
Fancy pasta shapes that can be threaded

1. Color the decals of the Bear family and then cut them out. (Ask a grownup to help you with the scissors.)
2. Thread one end of the yarn through one hole in the button. Make sure the button is in the center of the yarn, and knot the button in place.
3. Thread the pasta shapes onto the yarn on each side of the button. If you use different shapes, make sure both sides of your necklace are the same. Leave 3 to 4 inches of yarn at each end. Thread a small noodle on each end and then make a large knot.
4. Tie the two ends of yarn together in a tight bow.
5. Paste a decal on the button.

You can make a bracelet the same way using a shorter piece of yarn.

STOP!
Don't cut this page.
Do the activity on
the next page first.

35

Paper Plate Grizzbee

Here's a Grizzbee to make you flip!

You will need:
3 nine-inch paper plates

1. Color the picture of the Bear family and cut it out carefully. (Ask a grownup to help you with the scissors.)
2. Paste two of the plates together.

3. Cut out the center of the third plate and paste it onto the bottom of the other two plates.
4. Paste the picture of the Bear family onto the center of the third plate.
5. Decorate the rim of your Grizzbee.
6. When the paste is dry, ask a friend to play Grizzbee with you!

STOP!
Don't cut this page.
Do the activity on
the next page first.

CUT

Pomander Ball

Brother Bear made this present for Mama Bear's birthday.

You will need:
An orange, lemon, or apple
   (the fruit must not be bruised or soft)
Toothpick or blunt needle
Box of whole cloves
Sprinkling of cinnamon
Piece of aluminum foil large enough to
   wrap the pomander in
Piece of yarn or ribbon about a yard long

1. Punch holes in the fruit with the toothpick or needle.
2. Insert a clove into each little hole. (The cloves should be close together.)
3. When the fruit is completely covered with cloves, sprinkle it with cinnamon. Then wrap it in the aluminum foil and leave it in a dry spot for 2—3 weeks.
4. After 2—3 weeks unwrap the pomander. (You will find that it has shrunk.)
5. Tie the ribbon around the pomander, making sure to leave a hanging loop. Give it to someone you love!

Bear Family Finger Puppets

1. Color the Bear family.
2. Carefully cut out the figures and tabs.
(Ask a grownup to help you with the scissors.)
3. Wrap the tabs around your index and middle fingers, overlapping the tabs so that the puppets fit snugly. Secure the tabs with tape.

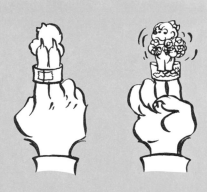

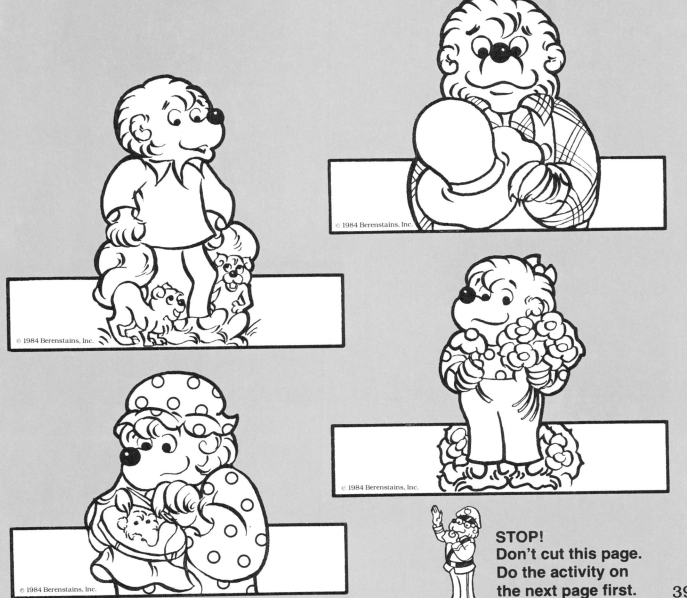

© 1984 Berenstains, Inc.

© 1984 Berenstains, Inc.

© 1984 Berenstains, Inc.

© 1984 Berenstains, Inc.

STOP!
Don't cut this page.
Do the activity on
the next page first.

39

School Bus

Brother and Sister Bear and their friends go to school in the yellow school bus. You can make the school bus and help them get to school.

   Color the bus and all the people in it. Cut the bus out carefully. (Ask a grownup to help you with the scissors.) Fold and paste or tape the bus where marked.

40

Bear Country Schoolhouse

1. Color and then cut out all the parts of the schoolhouse here and on pages 45 and 47. (Ask a grownup to help you with the scissors.)
2. Fold along all the dotted lines.

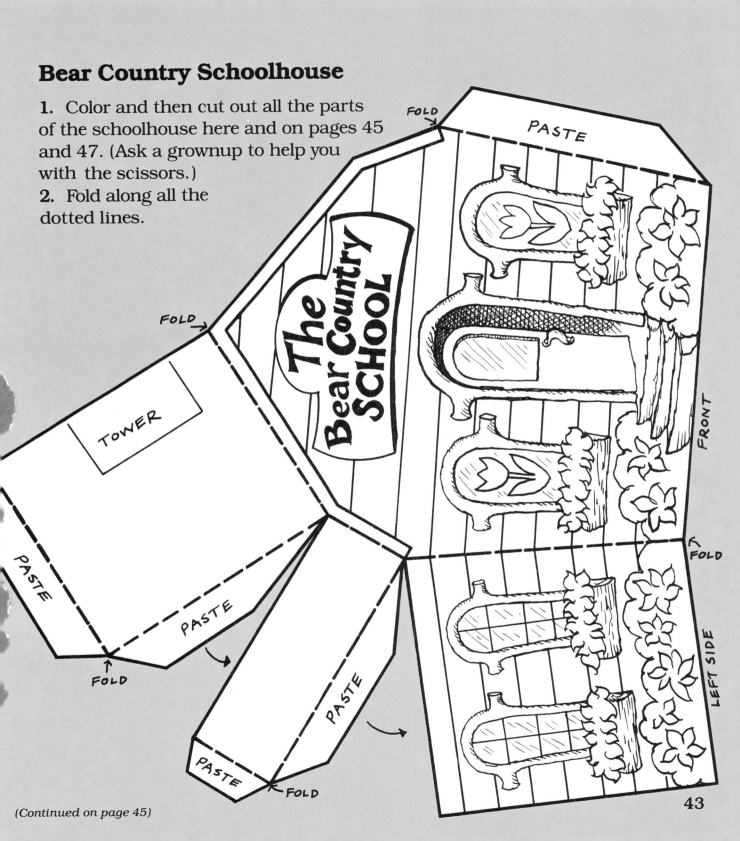

(Continued on page 45)

43

PASTE

PASTE

The
Bear Country
SCHOOL

© 1984 Berenstains, Inc.

44

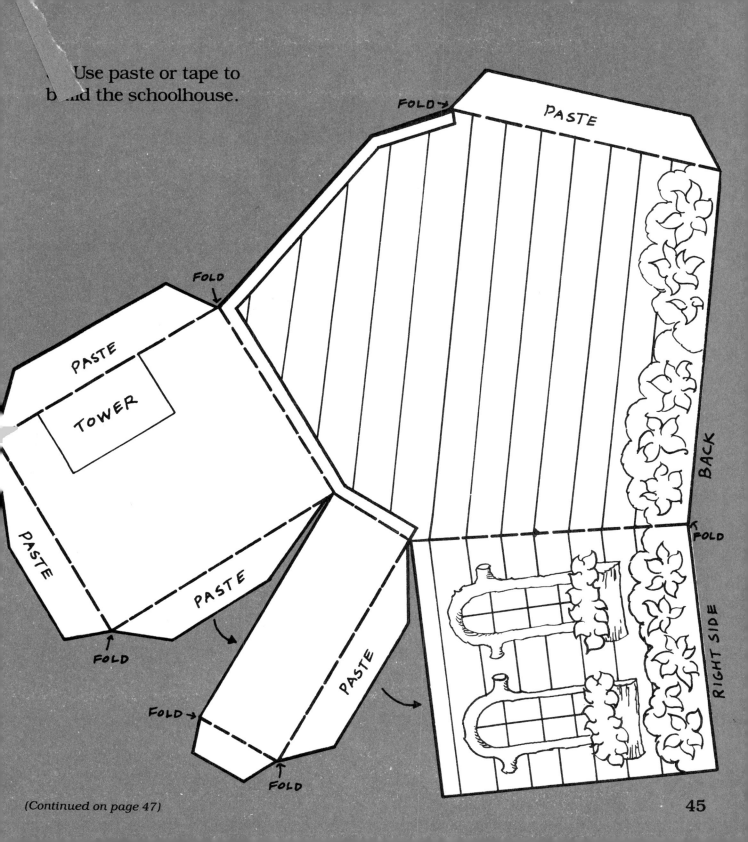

Use paste or tape to build the schoolhouse.

FOLD →

PASTE

FOLD

FOLD

PASTE

TOWER

PASTE

PASTE

FOLD

FOLD →

PASTE

FOLD

BACK

FOLD

RIGHT SIDE

(Continued on page 47)

45

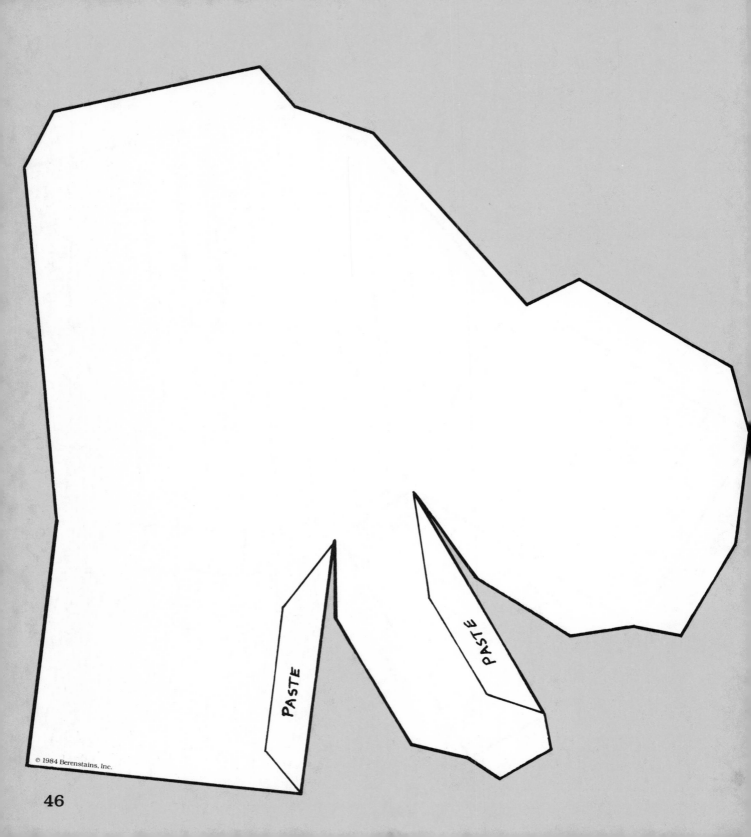

PASTE

PASTE

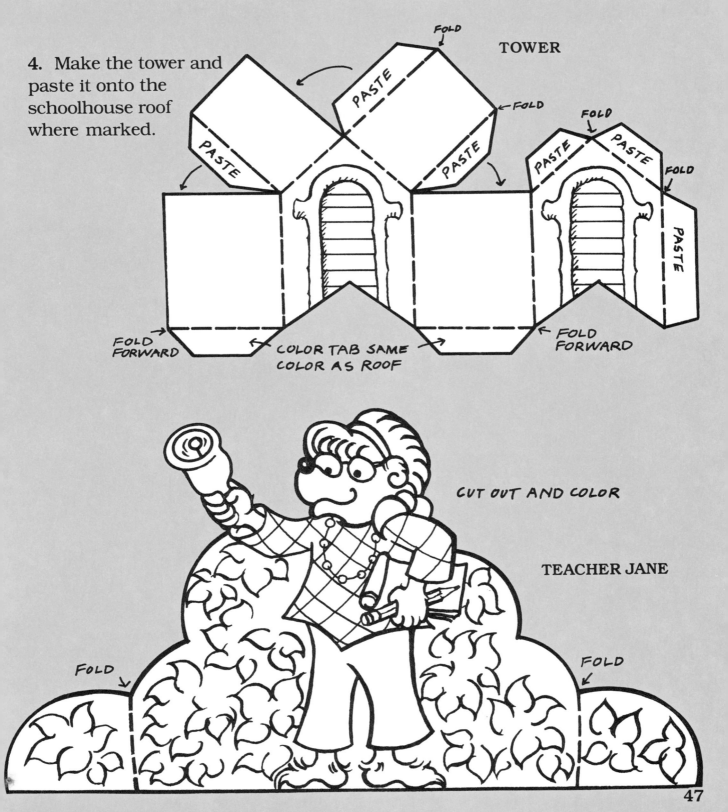

4. Make the tower and paste it onto the schoolhouse roof where marked.

TOWER

FOLD

PASTE

FOLD

PASTE

PASTE

FOLD

FOLD

PASTE

PASTE

PASTE

PASTE

FOLD FORWARD

COLOR TAB SAME COLOR AS ROOF

FOLD FORWARD

CUT OUT AND COLOR

TEACHER JANE

FOLD

FOLD

47

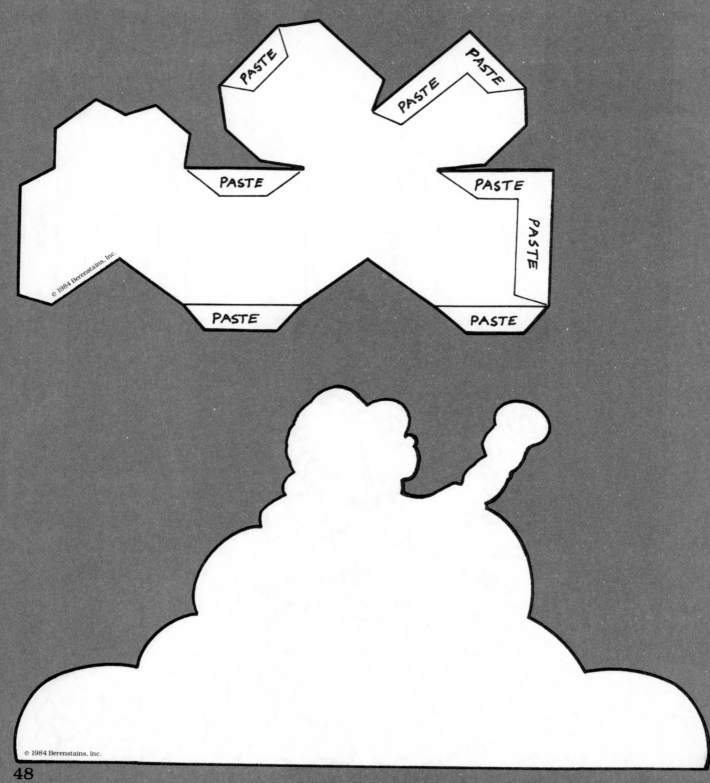

PASTE PASTE PASTE
PASTE PASTE
PASTE
PASTE PASTE

© 1984 Berenstains, Inc.

© 1984 Berenstains, Inc.

48

Bear Marks

Sister and Brother Bear call their bookmarks bear marks.
Here are some for you!

Color both sides of the bear marks and then cut them
out. (Ask a grownup to help you with the scissors.)

This bear mark belongs to:

49

Read

This bear mark belongs to:

BEAR MARK

Papa Bear Hand Puppet

Papa Bear always has a lot to say. Now you can help him talk!

You will need:
A sock the same color as Papa Bear
A piece of dark brown felt
Scraps of felt: orange, white, black, red, pink,
   and some the same color as the sock
A small black pom-pom if you have one

1. Cut page 53 from the book and cut out the pattern
pieces (ask a grownup to help you with the scissors).
2. Pin each pattern piece to the right color felt and then
cut out each piece of the puppet (ask a grownup for help).
Remember to cut 2 hats.
3. Remove the paper patterns after you've cut each piece.
4. Glue the two pieces of hat together. Use a lot of
glue so that the hat will be stiff when the glue dries.

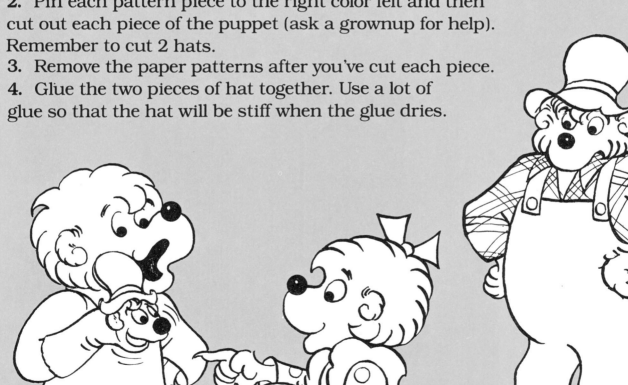

(Continued on page 52)

51

5. Glue the hatband into position.

6. Use the hat pattern as a guide and glue Papa's curl under the brim of his hat.

7. Glue the pupils onto the eyes.

8. Glue the tonsils onto the mouth. Use the mouth pattern as a guide.

9. Put your hand into the sock to see where the mouth goes (between heel and toe of the sock) and glue the mouth in place.

10. Take your hand out of the sock and glue the pom-pom, or a piece of black felt, onto the sock to make the nose.

11. Glue the eyes into position and then glue the eyebrows into place.

12. Glue the ears on either side of the face. *Be sure to put glue on only the front half of the ears.*

13. *Put glue on the back of the hat brim only* and glue hat onto sock.

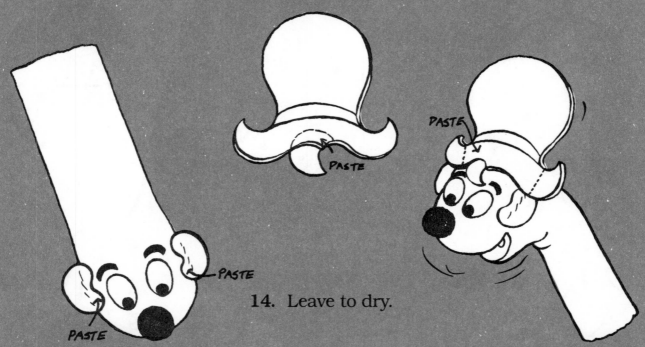

14. Leave to dry.

52

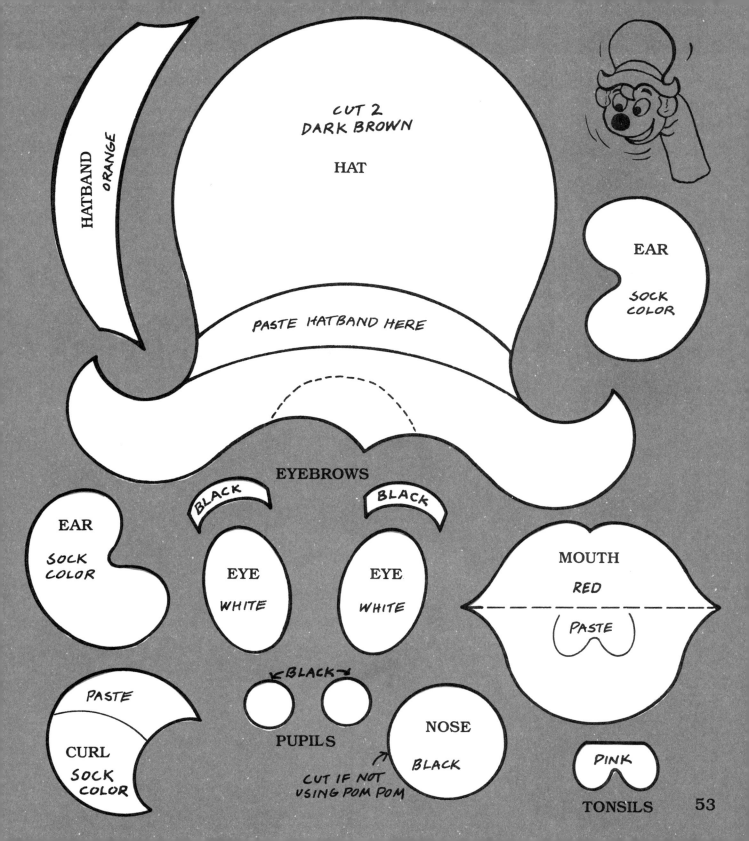

HATBAND ORANGE

CUT 2
DARK BROWN

HAT

PASTE HATBAND HERE

EAR

SOCK COLOR

EYEBROWS

BLACK

BLACK

EAR

SOCK COLOR

EYE

WHITE

EYE

WHITE

MOUTH

RED

PASTE

PASTE

CURL

SOCK COLOR

BLACK

PUPILS

NOSE

BLACK

CUT IF NOT
USING POM POM

PINK

TONSILS

53

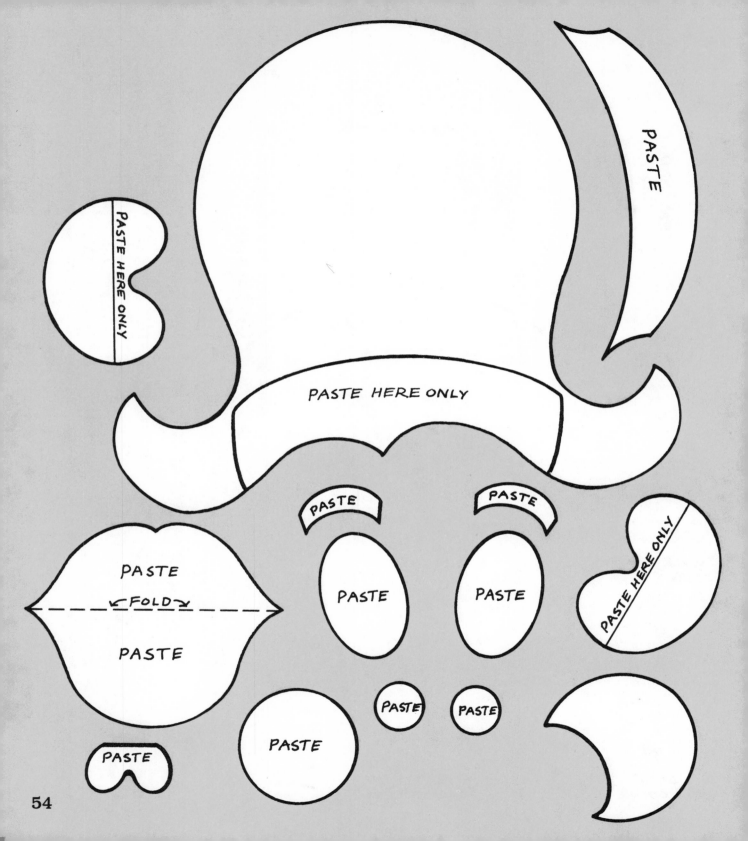

54

Bear Country Mobile

You will need:
A twig or a wire clothes hanger
5 pieces of string of different lengths, and
  a piece of string or yarn to hang your mobile

FOLD

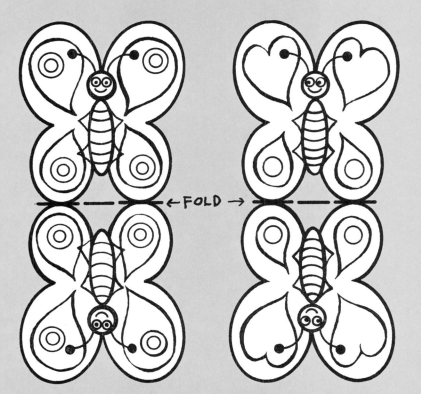

← FOLD →

1. Color the different parts of the mobile here and on page 57.
2. Carefully cut out each piece. (Ask a grownup to help you with the scissors.)

55

(Continued on page 57)

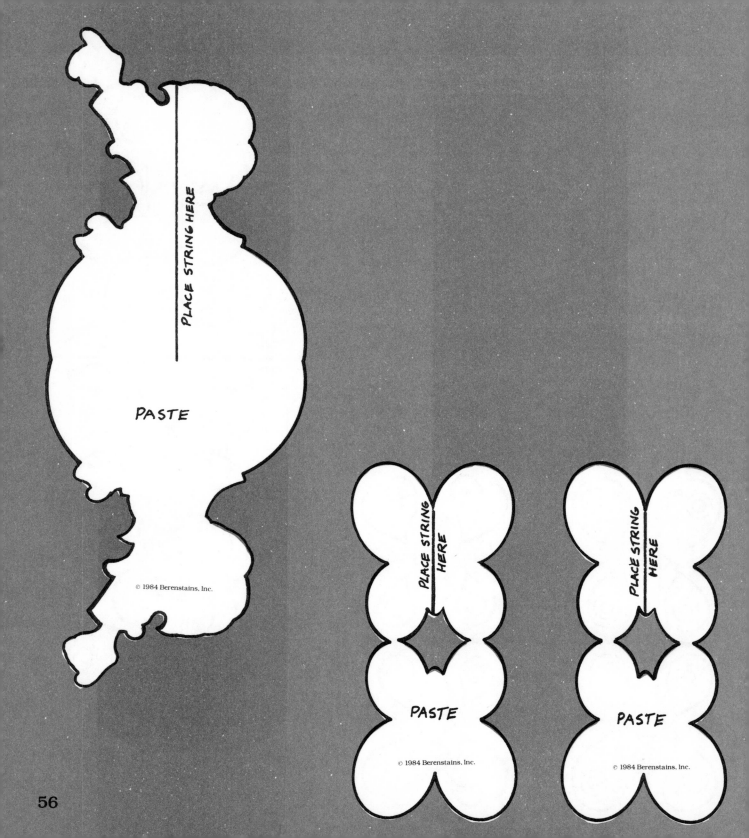

PLACE STRING HERE

PASTE

© 1984 Berenstains, Inc.

PLACE STRING HERE

PASTE

© 1984 Berenstains, Inc.

PLACE STRING HERE

PASTE

© 1984 Berenstains, Inc.

3. Put paste on the back of each mobile piece. Then place a piece of string on the back where marked.

4. Fold each mobile piece along dotted line. (Make sure the edges match.)

5. Tie each part of the mobile to the twig or hanger (be sure to leave enough space between each string so that they hang freely). Tie on the hanging string.

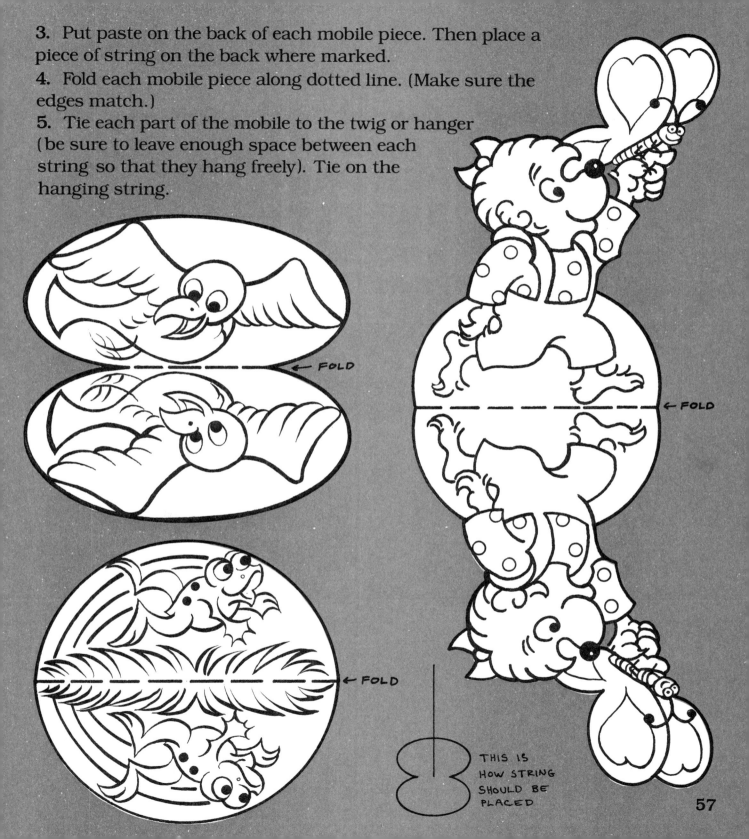

← FOLD

← FOLD

← FOLD

THIS IS HOW STRING SHOULD BE PLACED

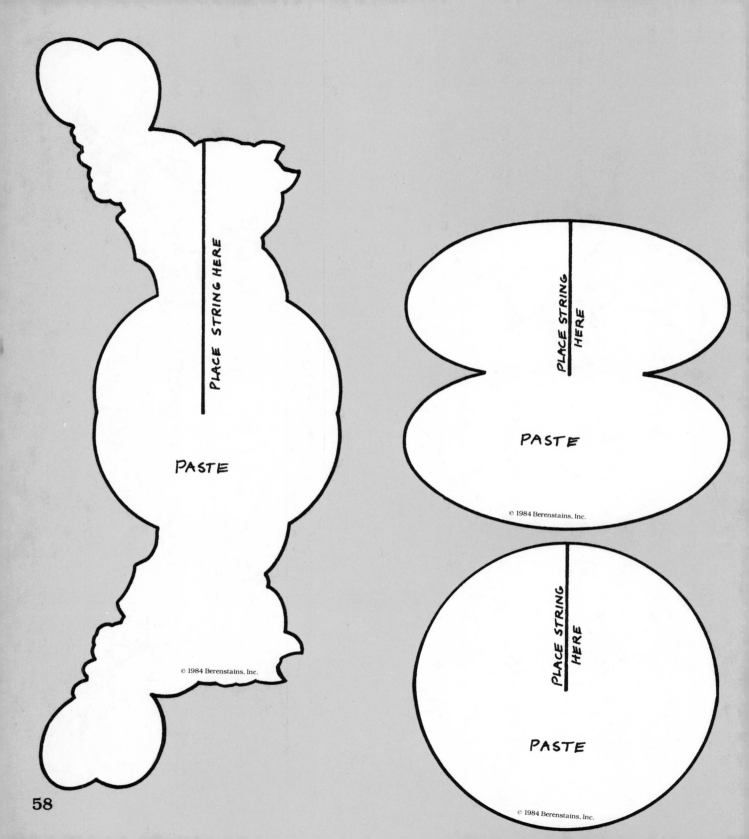

PLACE STRING HERE

PASTE

PLACE STRING HERE

PASTE

© 1984 Berenstains, Inc.

PLACE STRING HERE

PASTE

© 1984 Berenstains, Inc.

© 1984 Berenstains, Inc.

Tops to Spin

Make a family of spinning tops!

You will need:
Thin cardboard
4 toothpicks

1. Color the pictures on the tops.
2. Cut this page from the book and paste it onto the cardboard. (Ask a grownup to help with the scissors.)
3. When the paste is dry cut out the tops.
4. Push a toothpick through the center of each top where marked and add a dab of paste. Let dry.

© 1984 Berenstains, Inc.

CUT ON THIS LINE

See which Bear can spin for the longest time.

STOP!
Don't cut this page. Do the activity on the next page first.

59

Papa Bear's Kite

Papa Bear thinks he is a great kite flier. Build this kite and make Papa Bear fly!

You will need:
Clean brown shopping bag (cut open) or piece of paper 20 inches by 26 inches
Ruler
2 spruce sticks, one $3/8 \times 1/8 \times 20$ inches, and the other $1/4 \times 1/4 \times 26$ inches
Ball of kite string (you can buy the sticks and the kite string at a hobby store)
Some strips of crepe paper or cloth

1. Lay the paper flat on your work area.
2. Use the ruler to mark out a grid of 2-inch squares on the paper (ask a grownup to help you).
3. Copy the picture of Papa Bear square by square, onto the grid, and then color it.
4. Use the ruler to draw the straight outlines.
5. Cut out the kite. Don't forget to cut out the two little holes in the kite face. (Ask a grownup to help you with the scissors.) Now make the kite frame.

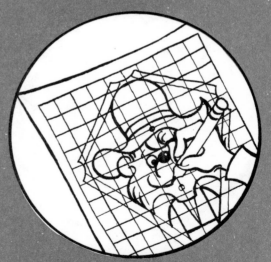

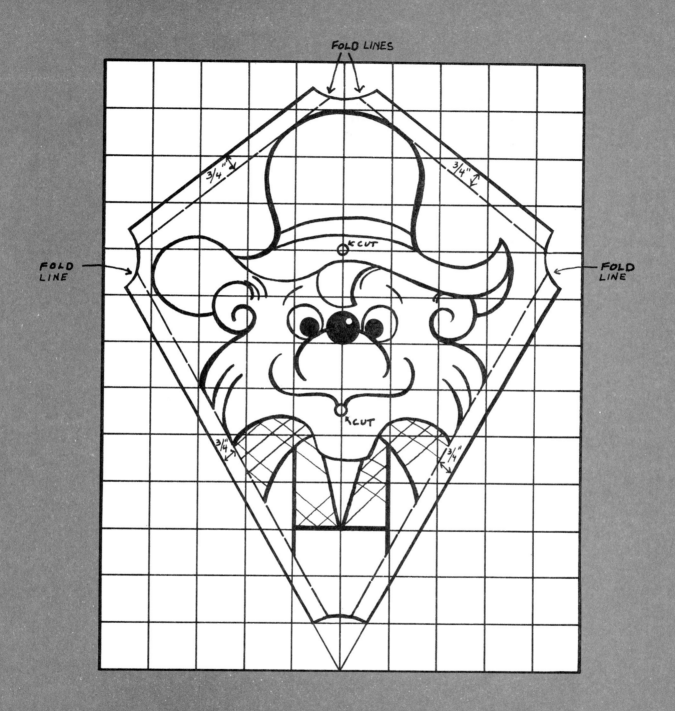

FOLD LINES

FOLD
LINE

FOLD
LINE

3/4"

3/4"

3/4"

3/4"

CUT

CUT

(Continued on pages 62 and 63)

6. On the longer spruce stick (the spine) make a mark 8 inches from one end. Make a second mark ¼ inch below the first.

7. Mark the center of the second spruce stick.

8. Center the second stick (the cross stick) on the spine, between the two marks.

9. Tie the two sticks together with a wire twister.

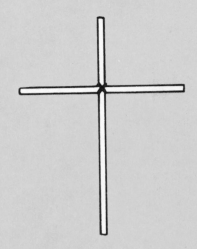

10. Cut a notch in the ends of each stick (ask a grownup to help you).

11. Run a length of string from tip to tip of the sticks, making sure to slip the string into the notches. The string must be taut but not so tight that it makes the sticks bend. (Be sure that the sticks remain at right angles to each other.) Tie the string firmly at the bottom.

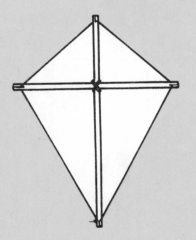

12. Lay the picture of Papa Bear face down on your work area and center the kite frame on it.

13. Carefully fold and paste the ¾-inch overlap over the string. Let dry.

14. Tie a string to one end of the cross stick and pull it tightly so that the stick bows a little. Then, with the stick bowed, tie the other end of the string to the other end of the cross stick.

15. To make the bridle: With the picture facing you, pass one end of the string through the top hole in the paper and tie it to the spine above the cross stick. Pass the other end of the string through the bottom hole in the paper and tie it to the vertical stick.

16. Tie the kite string to the middle of the bridle string.

17. Tie a length of string for the kite tail to the bottom of the kite and add pieces of crepe paper or cloth to the tail.

Wait for a windy day and have fun!

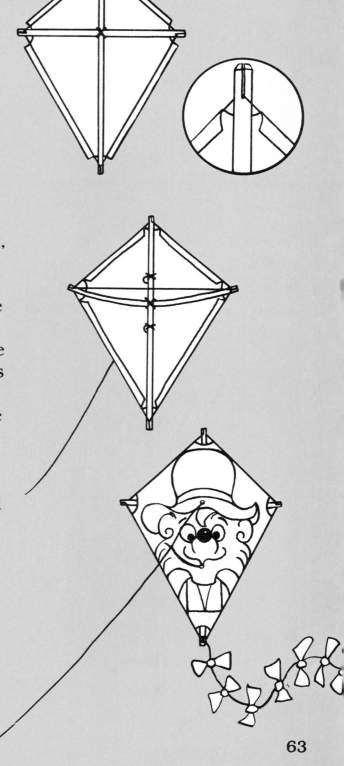

63

Answers

page 16

A P **R** o n

B A L L O o n

B o n **E**

D o n **K E Y**

L E M o n

M O o n

L I o n

T E L E P H o n **E**

page 30

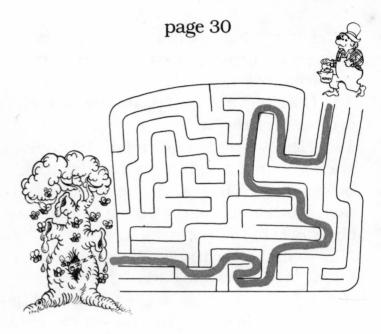

page 42

S R C H A L K
T E A C H E R O
O C L A S S O
R E A D B O W
Y S M E U U E
E S O S S I M
B O O K S Z O
P E N C I L H